One Giant Leap

From early astronomers to the historic day when astronaut Neil Armstrong made the first footprint on the moon, *One Giant Leap* will provide you with all you need to become the complete moon expert.

It's packed with amazing lunar facts, details of spaceflight programmes and lunar landings, spacecraft data, myths and legends – including the first ever printed science fiction story.

An intergalactic space quiz adds to the fun in this book celebrating man's first moon landing.

One Giant Leap

Sally Tagholm

Illustrated by David Farris

KNIGHT BOOKS
Hodder and Stoughton

Copyright © Sally Tagholm 1989
Illustrations copyright © Hodder and
Stoughton 1989

*First published in Great Britain in
1989 by Knight Books*

British Library CIP

Tagholm, Sally
  One giant leap
  1. Moon
  I. Title
  523.3

  ISBN 0-340-50619-9

Printed and bound in Great Britain
for Hodder and Stoughton
Paperbacks, a division of Hodder
and Stoughton Ltd., Mill Road,
Dunton Green, Sevenoaks, Kent.
TN13 2YA. (Editorial Office:
47 Bedford Square, London
WC1B 3DP) by Richard Clay Ltd.,
Bungay, Suffolk. Photoset by
Rowland Phototypesetting Ltd., Bury
St Edmunds, Suffolk.

For Tom, Hugo and Theo
and Happy Birthday, Emma

Introduction

The most famous footprint in the Universe is twenty years old. On Monday July 21st 1969, U.S. astronauts Neil Armstrong and 'Buzz' Aldrin landed on the Moon with the historic words, 'That's one small step for man, one giant leap for mankind.'

They unveiled a plaque, which said:
'HERE MEN FROM THE PLANET EARTH FIRST SET FOOT UPON THE MOON JULY 1969. WE CAME IN PEACE FOR ALL MANKIND.'

The Moon has fascinated, inspired and challenged us for century upon century. It has been an object of worship and of intense superstition, as well as a measurer of time and a powerful influence on the natural rhythms of our own planet. From the early astronomers in ancient Greece to the space programmes of the 1960s, we have always wanted to know more about our next-door neighbour in space. After the "Eagle" landed in 1969 there were five more successful Apollo missions. Altogether about 850lbs of moon rock and soil were brought back to Earth and an enormous amount of information. But for me, even more exciting than knowing the exact age of the Moon, the precise definition of a zap crater – or what the astronauts ate for breakfast – were the weird and wonderful moon stories that have been written over the years. They describe novel and hazardous forms of flight, involving balloons, bone marrow, whirlwinds or wild swans, and they tell of extraordinary moon creatures and things from Horse Griffins and Cabbage Fowls to wasted time and talent.

Take one giant leap and discover for yourself all you'll ever need to know about the Moon – fact and fiction.

Sally Tagholm

Contents

The Moon, facts and figures

Lunar fact file	
Diameter	3,476 kilometres
Circumference	10,927 kilometres
Mean distance from Earth	382,176 kilometres
Surface temperature	+120°C (day) −153°C (night)
Gravity	$\frac{1}{6}$ that of Earth
Mass	$\frac{1}{100}$ that of Earth
Volume	$\frac{1}{50}$ that of Earth
Lunar day	14 Earth days
Lunar night	14 Earth nights
Mean velocity	3,680 kilometres per hour
Rotation around Earth	27 days 7 hours 43 minutes

The Moon is our nearest neighbour in space. Its orbit around the Earth is elliptic, or oval-shaped, so its distance from us is not always exactly the same. One complete orbit takes 27 days 7 hours and 43 minutes, and this is called the sidereal month. Although the Moon moves eastwards, we see it rising in the east and setting in the west because the Earth is turning on its own axis.

The length of time between full Moons is longer than the sidereal month because the Sun, Earth and Moon have to be in a straight line. This takes 29½ days because, as the Moon is orbiting the Earth, the Earth is also moving slowly around the Sun, so its position in the sky has changed slightly. This is called the synodic month.

We always see the same face of the Moon because it revolves once on its own axis as it orbits the Earth. The light and dark patches that make up the Man in the Moon are, in fact, highlands and lowlands, known as 'terrae' (lands) and 'maria' (seas). The surface was moulded over millions of years by a combination of volcanic activity and asteroid bombardment.

The terrae are pitted with craters of all shapes and sizes – from a few millimetres to 290 kilometres across – formed by the impact of meteorites and cosmic debris. Some are flat and smooth inside; others have huge mountain peaks. A few shine when the Moon is full. There are lots of different formations: mountain rings, crater-cones and crater-pits are just a few.

The maria are smooth dark plains, also pock-marked with craters, peaks and ridges. Their name is very misleading as there is no water on the Moon. It is a dry, dead world with no air, no wind, no weather. Micrometeoroids bombard the surface continually as there is no atmosphere to burn them up.

The Moon has no light of its own but reflects light sent to it from the Sun. Really, its power of reflection ('albedo') is very weak: only 0.07 compared with the Earth's 0.4. This means that Earthshine is much brighter than Moonlight!

There are 32 known satellites in the solar system belonging to six different planets. Compared with most of them, our Moon is extremely small, but compared with the Earth itself it is very large indeed. It has a diameter of 3,476 kilometres, which is 27.5 per cent of Earth's; this means that it is more than a quarter as wide as Earth.

Craters and co.

Walled plains	Huge circular areas surrounded by massive ramparts
Mountain rings	Smaller circles with high walls
Ringed plains	The high walls slope down to the floor of the crater, and are often terraced
Crater plains	Smaller ringed plains
Craterlets	Small craters
Crater cones	Small volcanoes
Craterpits	Simple, wall-less openings
Zap craters	Tiny, glass-rimmed craters in rocks
Crater chains	Lines of small craters
Crater rays	Bright, shiny surface streaks that radiate from younger craters like Copernicus and Tycho
Wrinkle ridges	Winding ridges on the floors of the 'maria' (seas)
Faults	Scarp-like dislocations of the Moon's crust
Straight rilles	Deep trenches between faults, like canyons that cross floors of maria and large craters
Sinuous rilles	Winding channels that slope down from small craters – possibly old lava channels or collapsed lava tubes
Breccia	Fragmented rocks, caused by impacts on the surface
Regolith	Upper layer of pulverised rock, meteorite fragments and glass particles. Fine-grained, but it also contains boulders and rocks

Gallery of gods

The Egyptian Moon god was called Thoth. He had a human body and the head of an ibis, on which he wore a full Moon in the arms of a crescent. He was represented at his sanctuary in Hermopolis Magna by a real ibis, who lived a life of luxury there. As the lunar god, Thoth measured time, which he divided into months and years. The first month was given his name and his chief festival was on the nineteenth, a few days after the full Moon. Thoth was also the patron of science and literature, wisdom and inventions. He was believed to have invented arithmetic, geometry, astronomy, magic, medicine, drawing and writing. As the inventor of hieroglyphics, he was called 'lord of holy words'.

The Moon god in Babylonia and Assyria was known as Sin, which came from an old word meaning 'lord of wisdom'. He was a very important deity, and his children were the Sun and Venus. He was usually shown as an old man with a long bright-blue beard wearing a crescent Moon above his horned tiara. His biggest temples were at Ur in southern Babylonia and Harran in northern Assyria. He measured time and was called the 'lamp of heaven'. He was the enemy of criminals because he lit up the night sky.

Apollo 8 astronauts went into Lunar orbit on Christmas Eve 1968. Live television pictures showed them preparing their Christmas lunch of dehydrated corn chowder, chicken and gravy, toasted bread cubes, sugar cookie cubes, cocoa and orange.

In Ancient Greece the Moon was personified as Selene. She was usually shown with the crescent Moon on her head, driving her two-horse chariot across the sky. Her brother was Helios (Sun) and her sister Eos (Dawn). She was worshipped particularly at new and full Moon. The hunting goddess Artemis, sister of Apollo, the god of light, was also associated with the moon in Greece – as was Hecate, a

goddess of the Underworld, sometimes called the 'invincible queen'. On moonlit nights she used to appear at crossroads with a retinue of ghosts and howling dogs. Offerings were made to her on the last night of each month. This was called 'Hecate's supper' and consisted of eggs, fish, black puppies and she-lambs.

The Chinese Moon goddess was called Ch'ang-o. According to legend she was the beautiful wife of I, the excellent archer, who long ago shot down nine suns from the sky, when they were threatening to shrivel up the world. As a reward the gods gave I the elixir of everlasting life, but when he was away one day his wife, Ch'ang-o, drank it. I was so angry that Ch'ang-o fled to the Moon and begged protection from the hare who lived there. From that day on, Ch'ang-o has lived with the hare in the Moon and I can only visit her once a month when the Moon is full.

Chinese Moon Cakes are filled with sugar, orange peel, almonds, lotus or melon seeds. They are eaten during the Moon Festival, which is celebrated at harvest time on the 15th day of the eighth Lunar month, when the Moon is at its very brightest.

Vera Historia (true history)

by Lucian (second century AD*)*

This is the first known science fiction story. The heroes are whisked to the Moon by a whirlwind and are caught in a war between the Moon and the Sun. They meet Horse-Griffins, who are men riding on huge three-headed vultures with wings the size of sails, and enormous Cabbage Fowls, who bristle all over with cabbages instead of wings and have quill feathers like lettuce leaves. Other odd creatures include Pea-Shooters, Garlickeers and Bowmen who ride into battle on fleas 12 times the size of elephants. Helmets are made of large beans and breastplates of unbreakable pea-pods.

Manners and customs in the Moon . . . roast frogs . . . liquid air . . . baldness a beauty . . . robes of glass . . . removable eyes . . . ears . . . a magic mirror

Everybody lives on the same kind of food. They light a fire and roast frogs, of which they have large numbers flying about in the air, on the cinders. While the process of roasting is going on, they take their seats, as if around a table, and snuff up the savoury steam that rises, and thus enjoy a sumptuous feast.

Their drink is air pressed into a cup, from which a dew-like moisture is distilled.

Anyone who is bald and hairless is reckoned handsome among them. Long-haired people are an abomination. And the opposite on long-haired stars or comets: long hair is considered a beauty. This I can vouch for, as I was told by some visitors from comets in the Moon at the time. I should add that they grow beards down to a little above the knee.

The Moon-men have no nails on their feet, and no toes.

When they are working or taking exercise, they sweat milk from every pore which is mixed with a few drops of honey to make excellent cheese.

They manufacture oil from onions, as clear and sweet-smelling as myrrh. Also, they have abundant vines that produce water. The berries of the grape are like hail, and it seems to me that, whenever a wind shakes the vines, the bunches break and the result is a hailstorm on Earth.

They use the stomach, which they can open or shut at will, as a wallet or pouch, placing in it all their necessities. There seem to be no bowels or liver within the stomach: all you can see is a hairy and shaggy interior, where their young can find a warm retreat from the cold.

The dress of the rich is of soft glass; that of the poor, of woven bronze – the country is rich in this metal, which they work by sprinkling it with water, as though it were wool.

As for their eyes, I shrink from saying anything, in case you think I am a liar, but feel I must tell you. A man can, at will, remove his eyes and keep them until he needs them again. Then he can reinsert them and regain his sight. Many people who have lost their own borrow from others.

Some – that is to say, the rich – have a stock of eyes stored away.

Their ears are leaves of plane trees, though some have them of wood.

When a man grows old, he does not die, but dissolves into air like smoke.

And I saw a wonderful sight in the Palace. A vast mirror lies over a shallow well. Anyone who goes down into the well hears everything that is said down on Earth. And anyone who looks into the mirror sees all the cities and nations of the world as if he were actually there. I saw my friends and my country, but whether or not they saw me I am not sure. If you do not believe me, go and see for yourself.

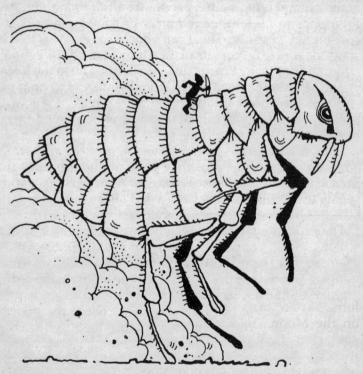

(*Taken and adapted from* **Lucian's Wonderland**, *a translation of* **Vera Historia** *by St J. Basil Wynne Willson, published by Blackwood 1899*)

Countdown Apollo

The background

On 25 May 1961 President Kennedy announced that the United States would land men on the Moon by the end of the decade. Six weeks earlier, a Soviet cosmonaut called Yuri Gagarin had become the first man in space, successfully orbiting the Earth once in his Vostock capsule. Before that, Soviet Moon probes had been streaking ahead: in January 1959 Lunik 1 had got within 5,000 kilometres of the Moon, in September 1959 Lunik 2 crash-landed near the crater Archimedes, and in October 1959 Lunik 3 went behind the Moon and sent back the first television pictures of the dark side of the planet.

The United States Moon programme was named Apollo – after the Greek god of light, the archer god, who shot his arrows from afar. But first came the Ranger, Lunar Orbiter and Surveyor programmes, paving the way for Apollo and the Moon landing.

> In 1956, the Astronomer Royal, Professor Wooley, said: 'All this talk about space travel is utter bilge.'

Ranger programme

The Ranger programme was designed to photograph the lunar surface to see if it was, in fact, possible to land men on the Moon. Television cameras were mounted on to spacecraft, which transmitted pictures back to Earth until they crash-landed on the Moon. The early Ranger crafts either missed the Moon completely or the cameras failed. It was not until July 1964 that Ranger 7 sent back the first close-ups (4,308 pictures altogether) of the Sea of Clouds, which was later to become the landing-site for Apollo 14.

Ranger 8 (February 1965) and Ranger 9 (March 1965) were also successful, and sent back thousands of close-ups of the Sea of Tranquillity and the crater Alphonsus. The closest pictures were taken from an altitude of only 550 metres and showed that part of the Moon at least was flat enough for a manned landing.

Lunar Orbiter programme

The main objective of the Lunar Orbiter programme was to find possible landing-sites for Apollo by photographing much larger areas of the Moon from a satellite in lunar orbit. The photography was much more sophisticated than the television pictures transmitted from the Ranger crafts. Between 1966 and 1967 there were five Lunar Orbiter missions, all successful.

Surveyor programme

The Russians were, in fact, the first to 'soft-land' on the Moon with Luna 9 in January 1966, beating the American Surveyor 1 by a few months. They both landed in the Ocean of Storms. Surveyor 1 sent back thousands of television pictures showing a flat surface, firm but finely grained, with some small craters. Larger rocks and boulders could also be seen, as could mountain tops 20 kilometres away. Surveyor 1 went on transmitting pictures for a while after the Sun had set and showed some of the Moon's surface illuminated by Earthshine. Surveyor 3 used a mechanical claw on a telescopic arm to examine the lunar soil under remote control from the Jet Propulsion Laboratory in California. Surveyor 5, which landed in the Sea of Tranquillity on 10 September 1967, sent back information on the composition of the lunar soil using an 'alpha-ray scatterer'. Surveyor 6 made a chemical analysis of the soil in a 30-metre-high wrinkle ridge in Central Bay, and the last mission, Surveyor 7, which was purely scientific, landed in highlands near the crater Tycho.

Mercury and Gemini programmes

Mercury was the first American manned space programme. It proved that an astronaut could survive in space for long periods of time. The Gemini programme went on to orbit the Earth in two-man spacecraft, to solve the problem of docking in space and to show that an astronaut could walk and work outside the spacecraft in space.

KREEP is moon rock which is rich in potassium, rare earth elements and phosphorus.
(There are two small pieces of Moon rock in London – one at the Geological Museum and one at the Natural History Museum.)
Lunar Rock is a fragment of KREEP!

Apollo programme

Apollo was a three-man spacecraft that consisted of three stages: the Command Module, in which the astronauts travelled to and from the Moon, the Service Module, which

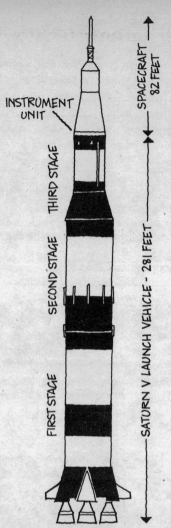

INSTRUMENT
UNIT

THIRD STAGE

SECOND STAGE

FIRST STAGE

SPACECRAFT
82 FEET

SATURN V LAUNCH VEHICLE – 281 FEET

housed the rocket engines, and the Lunar Module (in two parts – the descent and ascent stage) in which the astronauts were to make the Moon landing. The spacecraft was launched by the biggest rocket ever built – the three-stage Saturn 5, which was 11 metres high and weighed more than 300 tonnes.

Early Apollo flights tested the launch vehicle, the capsule and the equipment, but the first manned flight did not occur until 1968 with Apollo 7.

Lunar litter

The Moon was littered with American and Russian space probes by the time Neil Armstrong made the first famous footprint in July 1969.

Lunik 2 (389 kg)   Hit Moon on 13 September 1959

Ranger 4 (331 kg)   Hit Moon on 26 April 1962

Ranger 6 (365 kg)   Hit Moon on 2 February 1964 in Sea of Tranquillity

Ranger 7 (366 kg)   Hit Moon on 31 July 1964 in Sea of Clouds

Ranger 8   Hit Moon on 20 February 1965

Ranger 9   Hit Moon on 24 March 1965

Luna 5   Hit Moon on 12 May 1965

Luna 7   Hit Moon on 8 October 1965 in Ocean of Storms

Luna 8   Hit Moon on 6 December 1965 in Ocean of Storms

Luna 9   Soft-landed on 3 February 1966 in Ocean of Storms

Surveyor 1   Soft-landed on 1 June 1966 in Ocean of Storms

Surveyor 2   Crashed on 23 September 1966 south-east of the crater Copernicus

Lunar Orbiter 1	Deliberately crashed on 29 October 1966 on the far side of the Moon
Luna 13	Soft-landed on 24 December 1966 in Ocean of Storms
Surveyor 3	Soft-landed on 19 April 1967 in Ocean of Storms
Surveyor 4	Crashed (date unknown) before planned soft-landing in Central Bay
Surveyor 5	Soft-landed on 10 September 1967 in Sea of Tranquillity
Lunar Orbiter 1	Deliberately crashed on 9 October 1967
Lunar Orbiter 2	Deliberately crashed on 11 October 1967
Surveyor 6	Soft-landed on 9 November 1967 in Central Bay
Surveyor 7	Soft-landed in January near the crater Tycho

Orlando Furioso

by Ariosto (sixteenth century)

Everything that is lost or wasted on Earth is collected and treasured on the Moon. Not just kingdoms and riches but fame, which is destroyed by that old beetle Time down here on Earth. There are countless prayers and vows, tears and sighs, not to mention time and talent. In fact, you can hardly move for waste and are bound to find whatever you have mislaid or lost on Earth.

There are bribes hanging on gold and silver hooks, and flattery trapped in snares and camouflaged by flowering garlands. Greedy locusts burst with empty praise and the handcuffs of lost love sparkle with jewels. Bellows are swollen with the favours of princes and wasted kindness drips off a heap of broken soup-plates.

But, most of all, outnumbering everything else by far, there are bottles that come in all shapes and sizes. They contain a thin, light liquid called Common Sense, which evaporates very easily if not well corked. It has been lost in vast quantities down on Earth for all sorts of reasons – for love, money, honour, power, knowledge – or even poetry – but here on the Moon it is safely bottled and neatly labelled.

Time and tides

Long ago, the Moon's changing shape in the night skies was an obvious and convenient way of measuring time. The first calendars were made up of lunar months, which were 29½ days long, from new Moon to new Moon. This meant that the lunar year had 354 days in it, which made it 11¼ days shorter than the solar year, which had 365.

We use a solar calendar now, based on the time it takes the Earth to go around the Sun, and our months have nothing to do with the different phases of the Moon. But the Moon's phases are still an important influence in the natural world – not only on tides and fish but also on human beings. The female menstrual, or reproductive, cycle, when an egg ripens and is released from the ovary, is thought to be governed by the Moon. The cycle is usually between 27 and 30 days long (roughly one lunar month) and it takes its name from the Latin word for month, 'mensis'.

As the Moon goes around the Earth, its gravitational pull makes the tides rise. There are two high tides in each 24 hours: one when the Moon is at its zenith (highest point) and one when it is on the opposite side of the Earth. Twice a month, when there is a new or full Moon, there are very high tides (spring tides) because the Sun and Moon are pulling in the same direction. In between, there are neap tides, when the difference between high and low tide is much less. This is because the positions of the Sun and the Moon have changed and they are pulling in different directions.

Some sea creatures use the specially high tides to help them breed. In California tiny fish called grunion come ashore on spring tides to lay their eggs in the sand. The eggs lie safely buried until they hatch 15 days later and are carried back into the sea by the next spring tide. Other creatures are specially adapted to live in the inter-tidal zone between the land and the sea, washed by the waves that come and go: mudskippers, sandhoppers, lugworms, sea-slugs, sea-snails, cockles, mussels, starfish, sea-urchins and razor-shells.

Extravehicular mobility unit

(total weight 83 kg)

Extravehicular Pressure Garment: worn over the basic pressure suit, it was thermal, to protect the astronauts from extremes of temperature on the Moon, and micro-meteoroid-proof. It had 10 layers and was coated with Teflon.

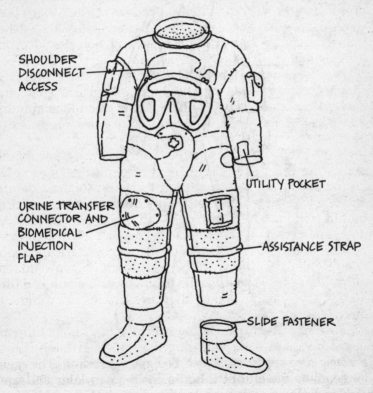

SHOULDER DISCONNECT ACCESS

URINE TRANSFER CONNECTOR AND BIOMEDICAL INJECTION FLAP

UTILITY POCKET

ASSISTANCE STRAP

SLIDE FASTENER

The first woman in space was Vanentina Tereshkova (26) in Vostok 6, in 1963.

Liquid cooling garment: made of knitted nylon, it had a network of plastic tubing through which cooling water from the portable life-support system (PLSS) was circulated. It was worn next to the skin under the extravehicular pressure garment.

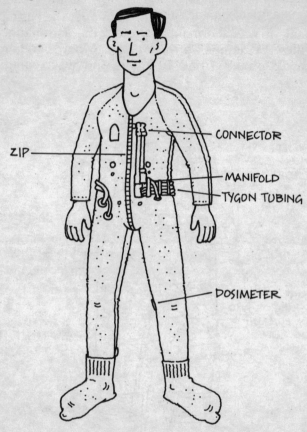

CONNECTOR

ZIP

MANIFOLD

TYGON TUBING

DOSIMETER

Portable life-support system: a backpack supplying oxygen and cooling water for the liquid cooling garment. The PLSS also included communications and telemetry equipment, displays and controls, and a main power supply.

Oxygen purge system: mounted on top of the PLSS, this was an emergency 30-minute supply of oxygen in two two-pound bottles.

Lunar extravehicular visor assembly: attached over the pressure helmet, it provided protection from micrometeoroids, heat, ultra-violet and infra-red rays.

Extravehicular gloves: thermally insulated to protect hands from hot and cold objects. The fingertips were made of extra-sensitive silicone rubber.

Communications carriers or 'snoopy hats': these included earphones and were worn with the pressure helmet.

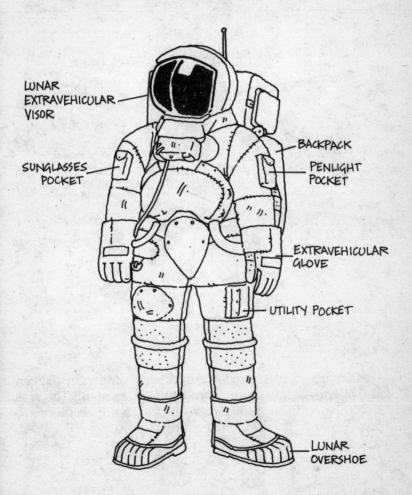

LUNAR EXTRAVEHICULAR VISOR

SUNGLASSES POCKET

BACKPACK

PENLIGHT POCKET

EXTRAVEHICULAR GLOVE

UTILITY POCKET

LUNAR OVERSHOE

MOONSPEAK

ONCE IN A BLUE MOON

ALMOST NEVER

TO CRY FOR THE MOON

TO WANT THE IMPOSSIBLE

TO BARK AT THE MOON

TO LABOUR IN VAIN

TO FIND AN ELEPHANT IN THE MOON

TO FOOL ONESELF

MOONLIGHTING

HAVING A SECOND JOB AT NIGHT

A MOONLIGHT FLIT

LEAVING HOME WITH ALL THE FURNITURE

MOONRAKERS

WILTSHIRE PEOPLE WHO TRIED TO RAKE THE MOON OUT OF A POND

MOON'S MEN

THIEVES AND HIGHWAYMEN

MOONSHINE

ILLEGAL ALCOHOL

MOONBEAMS

FAIRY FOOD

MOONFLOWER

LUNARIA OR HONESTY

MOONSTONE

JUNE BIRTHSTONE: IT MEANS THOUGHTFULNESS AND INTELLIGENCE

Early Moon-gazers: the Greeks

(with crater ratings)

Astronomers in Ancient Greece had advanced theories about the Moon which could not be confirmed for many centuries. At first, they used geometry to make their calculations, as algebra and trigonometry had not been invented. Much later, when the first Moon maps were being made, they were honoured by having craters named after them. Their importance is *not* always reflected by the size of the crater!

 Anaxagoras (500–428BC) was banished from Athens for his idea that the Sun was a blazing mass and that the Moon reflected its light. He also thought that the Moon had mountains, valleys and plains, just like Earth, and that lunar eclipses were caused by Earth's shadow.

 Aristarchus (310–230BC) maintained that the Earth moves around the Sun, as well as turning on its own axis. He tried to measure the relative distances of the Sun and Moon.

 Eratosthenes (276–196BC) was the custodian of the great library at Alexandria. He was a pioneer of science and astronomy and was the first person to measure the Earth's circumference. He made it 39,688 kilometres.

'O Moon, when I gaze on thy beautiful face,
Careering along through the boundaries of space,
The thought has often come into my mind
If I ever shall see thy glorious behind.'
(An anonymous house-maid!)

CRATER RATING
100 MILES

Hipparchus (about 140BC) was the greatest of all Greek astronomers. He invented trigonometry, introduced a magnitude scale for star brightness and compiled the first star atlas. He calculated that the Moon was 375,000 kilometres away and that its radius was 1,635 kilometres. He also suggested that its orbit might not be a perfect circle.

CRATER RATING
90 MILES

Ptolemy (about AD130) carried on much of Hipparchus' work and explained the apparent movement of the Sun, Moon and planets around the Earth. The Ptolemaic system was generally accepted for over 1,300 years, until it was challenged by Copernicus.

The age of science

(the sixteenth and seventeenth centuries)

Nicholas Copernicus (1473–1543) was the Polish astronomer who challenged Ptolemy's Earth-centred theory and paved the way for the modern view of the universe. He proved that the Earth was just one of the planets revolving around the Sun. His ideas, which were very unpopular with the Church, were kept secret until just before his death.

Tycho Brahe (1546–1601) built an observatory on the island of Hveen, which was given to him by the King of Denmark. He and his pupils calculated the positions of the Sun, Moon and stars with astonishing accuracy. They could measure angles to less than one-sixtieth of a degree.

Galileo Galilei (1564–1642) was a great Italian mathematician and astronomer. He made one of the first astronomical telescopes and saw mountains and valleys on the Moon through it. He described it as 'the most beautiful and delightful sight'. He also discovered Venus waxing and waning, Saturn's rings and Jupiter's four moons. His ideas were extremely unpopular and he was accused of heresy.

Johannes Kepler (1571–1630) was an assistant of Tycho Brahe and succeeded him as Imperial Mathematician to the Emperor Rudolph. He discovered the laws that govern the movement of the planets around the Sun and that their orbits are not perfect circles but ellipses. His mother was tried as a witch.

Sir Isaac Newton (1642–1727) was one of the greatest scientists of all times. He discovered the laws of gravity, which explained the relationship of heavenly bodies to one another. He described the Moon's irregular motions and the movement of the tides. He was Member of Parliament for Cambridge in 1688, Master of the Mint in 1699 and President of the Royal Society in 1703.

Spyglasses and Moon maps

from the Marsh of Decay to the Sea of Nectar

Galileo Galilei made the first astronomical spyglass in 1609; he got the idea from a lens grinder in Holland. The word 'telescope' was not invented for another two years, and at first the objects were known as spyglasses, optik tubes or perspective trunckes.

'First I prepared a tube of lead, at the ends of which I fitted two glass lenses, both plane on one side, while on the other side, one was spherically convex and the other concave.'

Looking through it, he discovered that the Moon was not smooth but covered with spots. He described the surface as 'uneven, rough and full of cavities and prominences, being not unlike the face of the Earth, relieved by chains of mountains and deep valleys'. He saw dark patches which he called 'maria' (seas) and lighter patches which he called 'terrae' (lands), even though he knew probably that there wasn't much water on the Moon – if any. He tried to calculate the heights of the mountains by measuring the lengths of their shadows.

The first detailed Moon map was made by Giovanni Riccioli in 1651. He named the mountains after ours on Earth (the Alps, the Apennines, the Pyrenees) and the craters after famous scientists and philosophers – although the size of the crater does not always live up to the importance of its namesake! The craters Copernicus and Kepler are quite large, as you would expect, but Galileo and Newton are quite small. Riccioli also gave some of the seas beautiful names, such as Tranquillity, Serenity and Fertility, which seem slightly out of place now that we know that the Moon is a dead, dry world of harsh extremes.

After Riccioli, the tradition of naming craters continued, and you can find the names of all the famous – and not so famous – astronomers, mathematicians, physicists and selenographers on the Moon. You might also notice the odd god, king, explorer, surgeon or optician if you look carefully. And if you are extremely observant, you might find a female astronomer!

Another famous Moon mapper, called Langrenus, named the smaller dark patches as bays, lakes and marshes. Their names are very different from those of the seas: the Marsh of Decay, the Marsh of Epidemics, the Lake of Death.

The first Moon globe was made by Sir Christopher Wren at Oxford in 1661, for King Charles II, who was patron of the Royal Society. It showed the spots on the Moon and 'the hills, eminences and cavities of it moulded in solid work, which if turned to the lights showed all the phases of the Moon, with the several appearances that arise from the shadows of the hills and valleys'.

As telescopes became more sophisticated, lunar maps became more and more detailed. The first really accurate one was produced in 1750, and a huge atlas in 1878 shows 32,956 different features on the Moon. Names, however, seem harder to find, and many craters – particularly on the far side of the Moon – remained anonymous.

In 1969 craters were named after living people for the first time: Armstrong, Aldrin and Collins.

Michael Collins (Lt Colonel), 38, 5ft 11ins, 165 lbs.
Command Module Pilot. He piloted the 3-day Gemini 10 mission, docked in orbit and worked outside the spacecraft, using a hand-held jet gun.

Large lunar maria

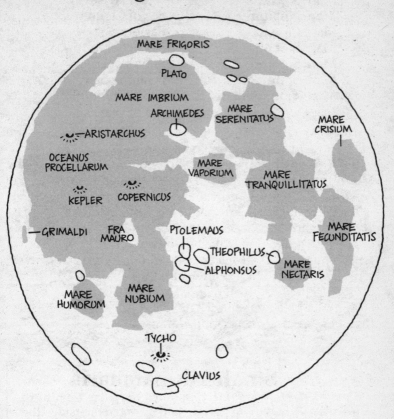

Oceanus Procellarum	Ocean of Storms
Mare Aestatis	Summer Sea
Mare Anguis	Serpent Sea
Mare Australe	Southern Sea
Mare Cognitum	Sea of Knowledge
Mare Crisium	Sea of Crises
Mare Fecunditatis	Sea of Fertility
Mare Frigoris	Sea of Cold
Mare Humboldtianum	Humboldt's Sea
Mare Humorum	Sea of Moisture
Mare Imbrium	Sea of Rains
Mare Ingenii	Sea of Ingenuity
Mare Marginis	Marginal Sea

Mare Moscoviensae	Moscow Sea
Mare Nectaris	Sea of Nectar
Mare Nubium	Sea of Clouds
Mare Orientale	Eastern Sea
Mare Serenitas	Sea of Serenity
Mare Smythii	Smyth's Sea
Mare Spumans	Foaming Sea
Mare Tranquillitatis	Sea of Tranquillity
Mare Undarum	Sea of Waves
Mare Vaporum	Sea of Vapours

Smaller lunar maria

Lacus Mortis	Lake of Death
Lacus Somniorum	Lake of Dreams
Lacus Veris	Spring Lake
Lacus Autumni	Autumn Lake
Palus Somnii	Marsh of Sleep
Palus Nebularum	Marsh of Diseases
Palus Putredinis	Marsh of Decay
Palus Epidemiarum	Marsh of Epidemics
Sinus Aestuum	Bay of Billows
Sinus Iridum	Bay of Rainbows
Sinus Medii	Central Bay
Sinus Roris	Bay of Dew

Space food

Space food must be lightweight, nutritious and tasty. It must not float around the Command Module and get into the equipment. Special menus were developed during the Gemini programme which provided the astronauts with at least 2,500 calories a day and produced as little waste as possible.

When the space menu was being prepared for Apollo II, the astronauts were allowed to choose what they liked from over 70 items. This meant that each man's menu was slightly different. For example:

Meal C: Day 2

Armstrong	Aldrin	Collins
Spaghetti with meat sauce	Chicken salad	Potato soup
Pork and scalloped potatoes	Chicken and gravy	Pork and scalloped potatoes
Pineapple fruitcake (4)	Beef sandwiches (6)	Pineapple fruitcake (4)
Grape punch	Grape punch	Grape punch

Because of the problems of eating and drinking in the weightless conditions of space, special freeze-dried, re-hydrateable food was developed. Water injected into the food bag, which was then kneaded well, produced a good meal in three minutes. The neck of the bag was cut off and the food squeezed into the astronaut's mouth. Afterwards, germicide pills were put into the bags to stop any leftovers going bad. More chewy food like sandwiches, brownies and cereal cubes came in bite-size pieces which were rehydrated in the mouth by saliva. They had a special crumb-proof coating.

Balanced meals for five days were packed for each man, but there was also a 'snack pantry' in case they got hungry in between.

Drinking-water in the Command Module came from a dispenser that squirted water as long as its trigger was held down. Other water for rehydrating food came from spigots at the food preparation station. One supplied water at about 68°C and the other at about 13°C; this meant that the astronauts could prepare a piping-hot meal and then wash it down with a cool drink. In the Lunar Module, Neil Armstrong and 'Buzz' Aldrin had to rehydrate their food with cold water from a hand-water dispenser that looked rather like a gun.

Packed lunch for the Moon landing was either bacon squares, peaches and sugar cookie cubes or beef stew, chicken soup and date fruitcake.

The Man in the Moon

Or is it a frog or a hare?

Long before Galileo looked through his telescope, people all over the world made up stories to explain the marks on the Moon. In India, Tibet, Japan and Mexico they saw a hare, in China a hare and a three-legged toad, in Malaya a hunchback under a banyan tree, in Scandinavia two children carrying a pail, in Peru the clawings of an ox and in New Guinea the fingerprints of naughty boys. The North American Indians saw frogs, giants, coyotes and trees, and the Maoris an old woman under a tree.

India: The Buddha, in the shape of a hare, offered himself to the chief god, Sakka, as a sacrifice. In remembrance, Sakka painted a picture of a hare on the Moon.

Scandinavia: Two children, Hiuki and Bil, were made to carry water all night by their cruel father; they were rescued by Mani, the Moon god.

New Guinea: Naughty boys opened the jar where an old woman kept the Moon. They tried to catch it as it escaped.

Maori: A grumbling old woman, going to fetch water, complained that she couldn't see where she was going when the Moon went behind a cloud. The Moon grabbed her – complete with water gourd, basket and the tree she tried to cling on to.

China: Ch'ang-o, who stole the elixir of everlasting life, was transformed into a three-legged toad. She lives on the Moon with a hare and Wu Kang, who was condemned to cut down cinnamon trees which grow as fast as he chops them down.

43

The Man in the Moone

or

A discourse of a voyage thither by Domingo Gonsales – the speedy messenger

by Francis Godwin (published 1638)

Domingo Gonsales arrives on the Moon after a bumpy flight that lasted 11 days. He travelled on an 'engine' pulled by a flock of gansas, a kind of wild swan, on their annual migration to the Moon.

He finds that trees are three times bigger than on Earth and animals and birds are enormous. Most of the people are about twice as big as us, and some are much taller – up to 8½ metres. Many of the taller people live an incredibly long time – some up to 30,000 Moones or 1,000 years. Smaller people appear to be nocturnal and to sleep for 13 or 14 days at a time.

There are beautiful lunar colours which are impossible to describe as they are nothing like ours on Earth. The same language is spoken all over the Moon and is made up of tunes and strange sounds rather than words and letters.

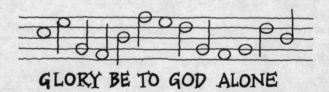

There is no rain, no wind, no summer, no winter – just perpetual spring. It is a land of plenty where people live in love and peace.

'Now when I shall declare unto you the manner of our travell unto the Palace of Pylonas, you will say you scarce ever heard any thing more strange and incredible.

'Unto every one of us there was delivered at our first setting forth, two Fans of Feathers, not much unlike to those that our Ladies do carrie in Spaine, to make a coole Ayrs unto themselves in the heat of summer. The use of

which Fans before I declare unto you, I must let you understand that the Globe of the Moone is not altogether destitute of an attractive Power: but it is so farre weaker than that of the Earth, as if a man doe but spring upward, with all his force (as Dancers doe when they shew their activity by capering), he shall be able to mount 50 or 60 foote [15 or 18 metres] high, and then he is quite beyond all attraction of the Moone's earth, falling down no more, so as by the helpe of these Fans, as with wings, they conveigh themselves in the Ayre in a short space (although not with the swiftnesse that birds doe) even whether they list.

'In two howers space (as I could guess) by the helpe of these Fans, wee were carried through the Ayre those five Leagues, being about 60 persons.'

Treaty of Principles governing the activities of states in the exploration and use of outer space, the moon and other celestial bodies

Outer space, including the Moon and other celestial bodies, is not subject to national appropriation by claim of sovereignty, by means of use, or occupation, or by any other means.

The exploration and use of outer space, including the Moon and other celestial bodies, shall be carried out for the benefit of and in the interests of all countries, irrespective of their degree of economic and scientific development, and shall be the province of all mankind.

Outer space, including the Moon and other celestial bodies, shall be free for exploration and use by all states without discrimination of any kind, on a basis of equality and in accordance with international law, and there shall be free access to all areas of celestial bodies.

There shall be freedom of scientific investigation in outer space, including the Moon and other celestial bodies, and states shall facilitate and encourage international cooperation in such investigation.

In January 1967 the United States, the Soviet Union and more than 80 other countries signed the Outer Space Treaty. It meant that the Moon belonged to everyone.

A voyage to the Moon

by Cyrano de Bergerac
(published 1754)

de Bergerac's first attempt at flying to the Moon, powered by bottles of dew attached around his middle, ended in disaster for our hero, and he landed in Canada. This is the story of his second launch.

I had made a Machine, which I imagined capable of bearing me to what Height I pleased in such a Manner that I did not believe there was anything wanting. Having seated myself properly, I push'd the Machine from the top of the Precipice; but whether my Measures were not properly taken, or that something was wanting in the structure I know not.

However, I fell pretty roughly into the valley. I soon got up and retreated into my Apartment, bruis'd from Head to Foot. After having anointed my Bones with Beef Marow and fortified my Internals with a Glass of excellent Cordial, I return'd to look for my Machine. But, alas, it was not to be found, for some Soldiers had carried it off to the Fort. They proposed fastening to it a quantity of Squibs, which, carrying it by Force aloft in the Air, would serve it instead of Wings and, indisputably, give it the Appearance of a flying Dragon.

In the mean Time, after haveing hunted a long Time for it to no purpose, Chance conducted me to it as they were setting it on fire. My anxiety at the Danger in which I saw my Handy-work was inexpressible. Transported with Choler, I flew upon the Soldier who was enkindling it and snatched the Match out of his Hand. Then, by throwing myself into the Machine, I endeavoured to disperse and extinguish the Combustibles which surrounded it. But my Arrival was too late. I had scarce set both my Feet in it when the Explosion of the Fire-works carried me and it to the Clouds.

To recollect what I thought at that Moment is impossible; the Horror of the Accident had transfixed my Soul and

deprived it of every Faculty. I mounted very fast, and I expected, at last, when the Force of the Powder was exhausted, to knock my Head against that of a Mountain. But, to my great Surprise, my Ascent was continued after my Chariot quitted me and fell to Earth.

This extraordinary Adventure filled me with unspeakable Joy. I was in Raptures to find myself remov'd beyond Danger. I began to search to find out what could be the Cause of it, when I perceived my skin vastly puffed out, and greasy with the Marrow which I used to foment my Bruises. I now reflected that the Moon, at that particular Quarter having a very strong Influence on the Marrow of Beasts, had sucked up that with which I had anointed my Body. Which Suction acted still more powerfully, the nigher I approached the Moon – nor did the interposing clouds weaken her vigour.

When I had travelled, according to the best Calculations that I could make, a little more than three Quarters of the Way between the Earth and the Moon, I felt myself turned suddenly topsy-turvey, for no apparent reason. I knew very well that I was not returning to our World, for I could see that I was travelling between two Moons, the Distance from one increasing as I approached the other. Our Globe now seemed like a large silver Plate and this gave me Hopes that I was going towards the Moon. My Opinion was confirmed when I remembered I had not begun to tumble till I had passed three Quarters of the Road. For, this I argued with myself, the Mass of the Moon being less than that of Earth, it follows that the Sphere of its Activity is of less Extent, and the Power of its Centre is not felt at so great a Distance.

At length, after falling a long Time, I found myself entangled among the Branches of a Tree, three or four of which I had broken by my Fall, and bruised my Face terribly against an Apple, which I smash'd, some of the Juice getting into my Mouth at the same Time.

A close encounter

13 July 1969	USSR launches Luna 15 'to conduct further scientific exploration of the Moon and near lunar space'
16 July 1969	US's Apollo 11 launched
17 July 1969	Luna 15 enters lunar orbit
19 July 1969	Apollo 11 enters lunar orbit
20 July 1969	Apollo 11's Lunar Module 'Eagle' lands on the Moon
21 July 1969	Neil Armstrong and 'Buzz' Aldrin take the first steps on the Moon Lunar 15 crashes on the Moon two hours before Armstrong and Aldrin take off to join their Command Module 'Columbia'

A lunar month 1989

with a sprinkling of superstitions

Monday 3 July — New Moon. Yet can't see it at all!

Tuesday 4 July — The Sun and Moon are pulling in the same direction so the tides are very high

Wednesday 5 July — Remember not to look at the new crescent Moon through glass – very unlucky! Make a wish when you see it, but don't tell anyone

Thursday 6 July — Flying insects are very busy when the Moon is new. Watch out!

Friday 7 July — *Never* look at the Moon over your shoulder

Saturday 8 July — When the Moon is getting bigger it is called a waxing Moon

Sunday 9 July — Good time for sowing seeds

Monday 10 July — You can see half a Moon now. The Sun and Moon are pulling in different directions so there are neap tides

Tuesday 11 July — When we can see half a Moon, the Moon can see half an Earth

Wednesday 12 July — Cut the branches of your tree now and they will grow straight

Thursday 13 July — Put eggs under the hen now and they won't go bad

Friday 14 July		When the moon is between half and full, it's called a gibbous Moon
Saturday 15 July		Not so many flying insects now!
Sunday 16 July		Never sleep in the rays of the full Moon
Monday 17 July		Watch out for witches on the eve of the full Moon
Tuesday 18 July		Full Moon: the Sun and Moon are in a straight line so tides are high again
Wednesday 19 July		Get rid of warts by catching the Moon's rays in a metal bowl and washing your hands in it
Thursday 20 July		People used to think that the full Moon caused madness. Hence the word 'lunatic' – from the Latin name for Moon, 'luna'
Friday 21 July		Happy twentieth birthday to the first footprint on the Moon!
Saturday 22 July		When the Moon is getting smaller it is called a waning Moon
Sunday 23 July		Good time for cutting anything that you don't want to grow again too quickly – like hair or corns!
Monday 24 July		Take in the harvest when the Moon is waning
Tuesday 25 July		You can see half a Moon again: more neap tides

Wednesday 26 July		Good time to spot the crater Copernicus. Its shadows are thrown from east to west
Thursday 27 July		Don't kill your pigs when the Moon is waning: the meat will shrink
Friday 28 July		Lucky time to move house!
Saturday 29 July		Tree-felling used to be illegal in France unless the Moon was waning
Sunday 30 July		Diving beetles get busy now as the new Moon approaches
Monday 31 July		Ranger 7 crashed on the Moon in the Sea of Clouds 25 years ago today
Tuesday 1 August		New Moon

Weather warning!
A hazy circle around the Moon is called a 'brough' and means that it will rain.

Adventure of one Hans Pfaall

by Edgar Allan Poe
(published early nineteenth century)

April 7:   Arose early and, to my great joy, saw the north Pole itself immediately beneath my feet. Alas, I was so high up that I could not make out the details. I deduced that at 4am I had reached a height of not less than 7,254 miles [11,674 kilometres] above the sea.

April 8:   The Earth now looked much smaller and was a brilliant yellow, almost painful to the eyes. The balloon hovered above the range of great lakes in North America and was holding a course that would soon bring me to the tropics.

April 9:   The Earth got smaller and smaller and was a deeper yellow now. At 9pm I was over the Mexican Gulf.

April 10:   I was aroused from my sleep at 5am by a loud, crackling sound. I was terrified, but could find nothing wrong with the balloon.

April 11:   The Earth looked tiny now and the Moon, which was almost full, was growing bigger and bigger. It was now very hard work to condense enough air within the chamber to keep breathing comfortably.

April 12:   I was delighted by a sudden change in course: having reached the 20th parallel of southern latitude, the balloon turned east at an acute angle and proceeded throughout the day in the exact plane of the lunar ellipse. The car started to vibrate, for no apparent reason.

April 13:   I was again very alarmed by that terrible crackling sound but still could find no explanation.

April 14:   The Moon was directly overhead. I was now convinced that the balloon was holding a direct course which would arrive at the Moon when it was nearest the Earth.

April 15: About 12 o'clock I heard that appalling sound again. It lasted much longer this time and got even louder as it went on. The car vibrated violently and something roared past, terrifying me with its flames and thunder. Afterwards, I realised that, in all probability, it was some mighty volcanic fragment ejected from the world I was so rapidly approaching, a meteoric stone.

April 16: Today, to my great delight, I beheld a very small portion of the Moon's disc protruding on all sides beyond the huge circumference of the balloon.

April 17: I awoke to find the surface of the Moon itself in all its glory beneath me. While I slept, the balloon must have reached that point in the journey where the attraction of Earth was superseded by the attraction of the satellite. It lay beneath me like a chart – still a long way away, but already its outlines were clear. The most extraordinary feature was the entire absence of ocean or sea – indeed of any lake or river! There were innumerable volcanic mountains, conical in shape, and the greater part of them in a state of evident eruption. I could judge their fury and their power by the thunder of so-called meteoric stones, which rushed upwards by the balloon with a frequency more and more appalling.

April 18: Today, I found an enormous increase in the Moon's apparent bulk and the increasing speed of my descent began to fill me with alarm. My theory had always been that there would be an atmosphere on the Moon that was dense in proportion to the bulk of the planet. The safety of my final descent on to the Moon depended entirely upon the support of its atmosphere. If I was mistaken, I would be dashed into atoms against the rugged surface of the satellite.

April 19: The surface of the moon was frightfully near but the pump of my condenser began to give me some indication that the atmosphere was chang-

ing. By 10 o'clock, I had reason to believe that its density had increased considerably and by 11 o'clock, I hardly needed to use the machine at all. At 12 o'clock, I unscrewed the condenser and unrigged the chamber. As I expected, it was somewhat difficult to breathe and my headache returned, but it was not unbearable. However, I was still descending with alarming speed, which seemed to cast some doubts on the validity of my argument, and I lost no time in throwing overboard first my ballast, then my water kegs, then my condensing apparatus and finally everything else in the car. But I still fell with horrible rapidity, and was now no more than half a mile [0.8 kilometres] from the surface. As a last resort, having got rid of my coat, hat and boots, I cut the car loose from the balloon and clung to the net hanging down from the balloon. I hardly had time to notice that the whole country, as far as I could see, was covered with tiny habitations before I tumbled headlong into the heart of an extraordinary city and into the middle of a vast crowd of ugly little people. None of them said a word but stood looking at me like a parcel of idiots. I turned away and looked up at the Earth – a huge, dull copper shield in the heavens overhead, tipped with the most brilliant gold.

Konstantin Tsiolkovsky worked out the mathematical laws of rocket motion in 1898. He said: 'The Earth is the cradle of reason but one cannot live in the cradle forever.'

The first footsteps

Neil Armstrong made the first footprint on the Moon at 03.56.20 BST on Monday (Moon-Day), 21 July 1969. It was with his left foot. Before leaving the Lunar Module 'Eagle', he had something to eat and put on his extravehicular activity suit and his extravehicular mobility unit. As he went down the ladder, he activated the television camera that would record his landing.

> **Neil Armstrong's heartbeats usually measured 77 per minute. When the descent rocket was fired, they went up to 110, and when he touched down on the Moon, they shot up to 156 per minute!**

He stepped on to the Moon and said: 'That's one small step for man, one giant leap for mankind.' Nineteen minutes later, 'Buzz' Aldrin joined him: 'Beautiful, beautiful. Magnificent desolation.' The television cameras showed a flat, crater-pocked moonscape, bleak in the Sun's harsh light, and strewn with rocks and boulders of all shapes and sizes. The surface was covered with a fine powder, rather like powdered charcoal, that stuck to their boots.

Their first task was to unveil a plaque which was attached to the ladder on the descent stage of the Lunar Module (which would stay on the Moon). It showed the two hemispheres of the Earth and said:

> ### HERE MEN FROM THE PLANET EARTH FIRST SET FOOT UPON THE MOON JULY 1969 AD. WE CAME IN PEACE FOR ALL MANKIND

They also took a silicon disc bearing microcircuit goodwill messages from the heads of states of 73 countries, and medals belonging to astronauts who had lost their lives before the Moon landing: Apollo astronauts Edward White, Virgil Grissom and Roger Chaffee, who died in a fire at Cape Kennedy two years earlier, and Soviet cosmonauts Yuri Gagarin, the first man in space, and Vladimir Komarav, who died in 1967 when the parachute of his Soyuz spacecraft failed.

Armstrong and Aldrin planted a US flag – three feet by five feet (0.9 by 1.5 metre) with a special wire stiffener along the top to keep it 'flying' in the Moon's airless atmosphere. It was difficult to get the eight-feet-high (2.4-metre) aluminium pole to stand up straight in the Moon's hard surface. Aldrin was then photographed next to it before starting his 'kangaroo-leaping' exercises.

The Apollo 11 astronauts spent more than five hours training for each hour of the 8-day mission.

President Nixon congratulated them from the White House in a historic telephone call: 'Because of what you have done, the heavens have become part of man's world. And as you talk to us from the Sea of Tranquillity it requires us to redouble our efforts to bring peace and tranquillity to Earth. For one priceless moment in the whole history of man, all the people on this Earth are truly one – one in their pride in what you have done and in our prayers that you will return safely to Earth.' Both astronauts stood to attention during this message and Aldrin, a US Air Force colonel, saluted.

The rest of their time outside the Lunar Module was spent setting out scientific experiments, collecting lunar rock and soil and taking photographs. Just under 2¼ hours after Armstrong made the first footprint, they climbed back into the 'Eagle' and, 21 hours 37 minutes after landing, they took off. They left the descent stage of the Lunar Module – complete with plaque – on the Moon. They also left equipment worth about £416,000 to lighten their load for lift-off – including cameras, boots, backpacks, breathing equipment, tools and urine bags.

Eight minutes later they were in orbit and, 70 miles above the Moon, they docked with 'Columbia'. Once they were safely back in the Command Module, the Lunar Module was jettisoned, to become another piece of space junk orbiting the Moon.

Neil Armstrong (38), 5ft 11ins, 165lbs. Civilian *Commander* of Apollo 11. He was a NASA test pilot, flying the X-15 rocket-airplane at 4,000 mph. On the Gemini 8 mission he carried a fragment of the Wright brothers' plane. His only hobby is gliding.

Edwin 'Buzz' Aldrin (Colonel), 39, 5ft 10ins, 165lbs. *Lunar Module Pilot.* Walked in space during Gemini 12 flight – he spent 5½ hours outside his spacecraft while it travelled three times round the world. Brilliant technician with a doctorate from MIT (Massachusetts Institute of Technology). Hobbies: running and scuba diving.

APOLLO 11's FLIGHT

BLAST OFF!

2·32 PM (BST)
WEDNESDAY 16 JULY 1969
(¾ SECOND LATE)

YOU'RE LOOKING GOOD!

MISSION CONTROL

50,000 MILES FROM EARTH, THE CSM AND LM PULL FREE OF ROCKET AND START 3·DAY JOURNEY TO THE MOON.

HALF WAY!

EARTH'S GRAVITY STILL AFFECTS THE SPACE·CRAFT AND HAS SLOWED IT DOWN TO 3,689 MPH.

BY **2·44 PM** APOLLO 11 GOES INTO EARTH ORBIT AT AN ALTITUDE OF 100 NAUTICAL MILES AND SPEED OF 16,500 MPH.

THE COMMAND AND SERVICE MODULES (CSM) SEPARATE FROM THE SATURN ROCKET.

FIRE!

MISSION CONTROL

ROCKET IS FIRED OUT OF THE WAY, INTO SOLAR ORBIT.

THE VIEW IS BEAUTIFUL— IT'S OUT OF THIS WORLD!

"BUZZ" ALDRIN SAYS. COLLINS DOES HIS FLOATING JOGGING IN THE BACKGROUND.

AT **5·16 PM** THE THIRD STAGE ENGINE FIRES APOLLO AWAY FROM EARTH TOWARDS THE MOON AT 24,545 MPH.

CSM TURNS THROUGH 180° AND DOCKS WITH LUNAR MODULE (LM), WHICH IS STILL HOUSED ON TOP OF ROCKET.

NEIL ARMSTRONG SAYS:

OUT OF MY WINDOW I CAN SEE THE ENTIRE CONTINENT OF NORTH AMERICA, ALASKA, OVER THE POLE, DOWN THE YUCATAN PENINSULA, CUBA, THE NORTHERN PART OF SOUTH AMERICA, AND THEN I RUN OUT OF WINDOW!

IN FLIGHT DUTIES

CHARGE BATTERIES
DUMP WATER WASTE
CHECK FUEL AND OXYGEN
NAVIGATIONAL SIGHTINGS
CHECK MEASUREMENTS

THURSDAY 17 JULY 1969
LATEST NEWSFLASH FROM EARTH.

THE USSR'S LUNA 15 SPACECRAFT HAS JUST ENTERED LUNAR ORBIT!

FRIDAY 18 JULY 1969
NEIL ARMSTRONG AND "BUZZ" ALDRIN CHECK THE LUNAR MODULE.

SATURDAY 19 JULY 1969
WITH 39,000 MILES TO GO, APOLLO 11 BEGINS TO FEEL THE MOON'S GRAVITY.

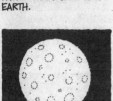

6.13 PM
DISAPPEARS BEHIND MOON AND GOES INTO LUNAR ORBIT.

TELEVISION PICTURES SHOW MOON'S SURFACE AND PROPOSED LANDING SITE IN *SEA OF TRANQUILLITY*.

6.47 PM
SUNDAY 20 JULY
LUNAR MODULE (LM) SEPARATES FROM COMMAND AND SERVICE MODULE (CSM) AFTER 12 ORBITS OF MOON.

AFTER SEPARATION THE LUNAR MODULE IS KNOWN AS "EAGLE" AND THE COMMAND AND SERVICE MODULE AS "COLUMBIA".

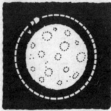

NEIL ARMSTRONG AND "BUZZ" ALDRIN PREPARE TO LAND ON THE MOON WHILE MICHAEL COLLINS ORBITS THE MOON IN *COLUMBIA*.

WE'RE OFF TO A GOOD START! PLAY IT COOL!

MISSION CONTROL

THE LUNAR MODULE WAS CALLED *"TRANQUILLITY BASE"* WHILE IT WAS ON THE MOON'S SURFACE. IT LANDED IN *THE SEA OF TRANQUILLITY*, FOUR MILES WEST OF TARGET, ABOUT 20 MILES SOUTH-WEST OF THE CRATER *MASKELYNE*.

THE AUTO-TARGETING WAS TAKING US RIGHT INTO A FOOTBALL-FIELD-SIZED CRATER, FULL OF BOULDERS AND ROCKS!

AT 300 FEET, NEIL ARMSTRONG TOOK OVER THE SEMI-MANUAL CONTROLS.

THE EAGLE HAS LANDED!

9.17 PM
(+42 SECONDS)
20 JULY 1969

WHEN THEY LANDED, IT WAS 0°F IN THE SUNLIGHT (90°F BY THE TIME THEY LEFT). IT WAS LUNAR DAY THROUGH-OUT THEIR STAY. PEOPLE ON EARTH COULD SEE A HALF MOON AND THE ASTRONAUTS COULD SEE A HALF-EARTH.

Apollo 11 scientific experiments

Laser ranging retro-reflector: this reflected a powerful laser pulse sent up from Earth. By timing its return (2½ seconds) it was possible to measure the exact distance between the Earth and the Moon within centimetres.

Passive seismic experiment package: this consisted of a set of weights hanging inside a cylinder and detected moon-quakes. It registered a tremor while the Apollo 11 astronauts were still on their way back to Earth, but no one is quite sure what it was. It could have been the Soviet craft Luna 15 crashing in the Sea of Crises. The equipment overheated and stopped working after 21 days.

Solar wind experiment: this was an aluminium foil banner which was set up to measure the gases that blast from the Sun at millions of kilometres per hour.

Altogether there were five more Apollo landings on the Moon between 1969 and 1972. The whole programmes cost $25.5 billion and brought back about 385 kilogrammes of rock and soil. The last three missions used the Lunar Rover, an electric car, which travelled at speeds of up to 13 kilometres per hour over the surface of the Moon. This meant that they could travel much further and collect all sorts of different samples.

Mission	*Date*	*Time outside Lunar Module*
Apollo 11	July 1969	2.2 hours
Apollo 12	November 1969	7.6 hours
Apollo 13	April 1970	mission aborted: explosion in Service Module
Apollo 14	February 1971	9.2 hours
Apollo 15	July 1971	18.3 hours
Apollo 16	April 1972	20.1 hours
Apollo 17	December 1972	22 hours

A trip around the moon

by Jules Verne
(published 1915)

The spacecraft was advancing rapidly and Mount Copernicus appeared before them, its top lost in an eruption of solar
rays. It rose to a height of 10,600 feet [3,231 metres] above
the surface of the Moon and is quite visible from Earth.
Astronomers can study it with ease, particularly during the
phase between the last quarter and the new Moon, because
the shadows are thrown lengthways from east to west. It
rises like a gigantic lighthouse on the part of the Sea of
Clouds which is bounded by the Sea of Tempests, dazzling
rays shining from the top and lighting up both seas. It has
been taken for an active volcano because of its extreme
brilliance but, like all on that side of the Moon, it is extinct.
Its diameter is about 22 leagues.

At this time, the spacecraft looked straight down over the
almost perfect circle of Copernicus and its steep escarp-
ments were clearly defined. At the bottom, as if enclosed in
a jewel case, two or three eruptive cones sparkled like
enormous dazzling gems.

Towards the south, the plain was very flat, without one
elevation, without one projection. Towards the north, on
the other hand, as far as the Sea of Storms, it resembled a
liquid surface whipped up by a storm, the hills and hollows
like frozen waves. Over the whole of this, in all directions,
lay the luminous lines, all converging on the summit of
Copernicus.

The space-travellers discussed the origin of these strange
rays, which only appeared when the Sun was in opposition
to the Moon.

'How have they tried to explain these lines before? There
must be a theory!' asked Michel.

'Yes,' replied Barbicane, 'Herschel thought that they
might be streams of cooled lava which shone when the Sun
beat straight upon them. But who knows?'

'Do you know what that plain reminds me of?' asked

Michel. 'With all those long, thin pieces of lava, it looks like an immense game of Spillikins! Seriously, though, they could be bones – and then this plain would be nothing but an enormous graveyard of the remains of thousands of extinct generations.'

The spacecraft advanced steadily and the landscape changed rapidly. At about half-past one in the morning, they caught a glimpse of another mountain. Barbicane consulted his map and recognised Eratosthenes. It was a ringed mountain, 9,000 feet [2,743 metres] high and one of the circles so numerous on the Moon. Barbicane explained an unusual theory about these put forward by the celebrated mathematician and astronomer Kepler in the seventeenth century. 'He thought that the craters had been dug by the Selenites as refuges from the solar rays, which beat down on them for 15 days at a time!'

'Interesting,' said Nicholl, 'but he probably didn't know the true dimensions of the circles. The digging of them would have been the work of giants, quite impossible for Selenites.'

'Why? If weight on the Moon's surface is six times less than that on Earth?' said Michel.

'But if the Selenites are six times smaller?' retorted Nicholl. 'And if there are no Selenites?' added Barbicane, putting an end to the discussion.

Space waste

Launch urine collecting bags

These were used during pre-launch and launch until the spacecraft was safely in orbit. They were Y-shaped bags which fitted on the inside of the spacesuit around the pelvic region. There were two openings: one, fitted with rubber sleeves, was for the urine to go in through, and the other was for emptying purposes. Once in orbit, the spacesuit unzipped to allow the collection bag to be removed and sealed off. The urine was then dumped overboard through the spacecraft urine dump valve in the Command Module and stored in the Lunar Module.

Urine transport system

This was used while the spacecraft was in orbit. It consisted of a urine receiver, shut-off valve, rectangular urine collection bags, urine sampler valve and a quick-connect fitting. The urine receiver was a roll-on rubber sleeve with a one-way check valve just inside the opening, which was forced open by the urine. A sampler valve, just behind the urine receiver, allowed the astronauts to take samples for medical examination when they got back to Earth. Otherwise, urine was emptied through the overboard dump system.

Defaecation collection system

Solid body waste (faeces) in space was much more of a problem, as it could not be flushed overboard like urine. Also, the faeces were weightless and therefore difficult to collect. The system consisted primarily of a strong, light-weight plastic bag about 18 centimetres wide at the bottom and 33 centimetres long. The opening of the bag was about 10 centimetres in diameter and was surrounded by a rim covered with adhesive tape with which to attach the bag to the body. Each bag contained a germicide to prevent the formation of gas and bacteria. After use, the bags were sealed and stowed away in empty food containers and taken back to Earth for analysis. Each astronaut was supplied with one bag per day, with a few extra ones for emergencies.

On Earth, a space-suit weighted 185lb and an astronaut approximately 165lb. On the Moon, each fully-equipped astronaut only weighed 58lb!

The first men in the Moon

by H. G. Wells (published 1904)

Suddenly the crack that had been admitting the light broadened out, and revealed itself as the space of an opening door. Beyond was a sapphire vista, and in the doorway stood a grotesque outline silhouetted against the glare.

We both made convulsive efforts to turn, and failing, sat staring over our shoulders at this. My first impression was of some clumsy quadruped with lowered head. Then I perceived it was the slender pinched body and short and extremely attenuated bandy legs of a Selenite, with his head depressed between his shoulders. He was without the helmet and body covering they wear upon the exterior. He was a blank, black figure to us, but instinctively our imaginations supplied features to his very human outline. I, at least, took it instantly that he was somewhat hunchbacked, with a high forehead and long features.

He came forward three steps and paused for a time. His movements seemed absolutely noiseless. Then he came forward again. He walked like a bird, his feet fell one in front of the other. He stepped out of the ray of light that came through the doorway, and it seemed as though he vanished altogether in the shadow.

For a moment my eyes sought him in the wrong place, and then I perceived him standing facing us both in the full light. Only the human features I had attributed to him were not there at all! Of course I ought to have expected that, only I didn't. It came to me as an absolute, for a moment an overwhelming, shock. It seemed as though it wasn't a face, as though it must needs be a mask, a horror, a deformity, that would presently be disavowed or explained. There was no nose, and the thing had dull bulging eyes at the side – in the silhouette I had supposed they were ears. There were no ears. I have tried to draw one of these heads, but I cannot. There was a mouth, downwardly curved, like a human mouth in a face that stares ferociously.

The neck on which the head was poised was jointed in three places, almost like the short joints in the leg of a crab. The joints of limbs I could not see, because of the puttee-like straps in which they were swathed, and which formed the only clothing the being wore. There the thing was, looking at us.

Apollo and after

After the Apollo 11 astronauts splashed down in the Pacific Ocean, they were picked up by the aircraft-carrier USS *Hornet* and immediately put into quarantine. This lasted for a total of 21 days from the time they took off from the Moon. The rocks and soil they brought back were also quarantined in case they contained unknown Moon germs. When they were declared safe, samples were sent off to scientists around the world for examination. There was enormous excitement about what the Moon rocks proved.

By the end of the entire Apollo programme, a huge amount of information had been gathered, although the exact origin of the Moon remained uncertain. We now know that:

1 Solid rocks first crystallised on the Moon at least 4,600 million years ago.

2 There was huge volcanic activity on the Moon between 4,600 million and 3,800 million years ago.

3 The maria (seas) were formed after this and filled with molten lava after another period of volcanic activity between 3,800 million and 3,200 million years ago.

4 There is no evidence of water, fossils or life at any time in the Moon's history.

5 Moon rocks are chemically different from igneous rocks on Earth, which suggests that the Moon was never part of Earth but had a separate origin.

6 There is very little volcanic activity on the Moon now.

7 The Moon is moving very slowly away from Earth.

Moon Party

If your birthday falls in the month of July – why not throw a Moon party?

With the help of an adult – try making these:

Moon Rock cakes

Ingredients

225g plain flour
1 teaspoon baking powder
100g margarine or butter
75g sugar

100g raisins
1 beaten egg
2 tablespoons milk

Set the oven to Gas Mark 7 or 220°C (425°F). Grease a large baking tray. Sift the flour and baking powder into a bowl and rub in the fat until the mixture resembles breadcrumbs. Stir in the sugar and raisins and egg. Add the milk and mix into a stiff dough. Place tablespoons of mixture on to the tray and bake for 20 minutes until golden.

Krispie Craters

Ingredients

175g butter
50g sugar
30ml golden syrup
175g Rice Krispies
50g chocolate powder

Melt the butter, sugar and syrup over a low heat. Mix in the chocolate powder and then the Rice Krispies. Place spoonfuls on to a tray and make a 'well' in the middle of each using a spoon. Leave to set.

Astro Biscuits

Ingredients

100g plain flour
100g margarine/butter
25g caster sugar
1 beaten egg

Sift flour into a bowl and rub in the fat until the mixture resembles breadcrumbs. Stir in the sugar and egg, forming a dough. Knead the dough on a floured surface until smooth enough to roll out. Cut out star shapes and planet circles and moon crescents, using cutters if you have them.

Special Moon Cakes are made for the Chinese Moon Festival. They used to come in different shapes like pagodas, fish or animals. Now they are usually round and filled with a puree of beans and lotus seeds.

Bake Gas Mark 4 or 180°C (350°F) for 15 minutes. When cool, ice them and decorate with silver balls, sugar strands, etc.

For a special birthday cake, how about a **Lunar Landscape**?

Ingredients

125g flour – sifted
125g margarine/butter
125g caster sugar
2 eggs
2 tablespoons water

For the frosting:
1 egg white
75g caster sugar
2 tablespoons water
pinch of salt

Set oven to Gas Mark 3 or 160°C (325°F). Put all the ingredients into a bowl and beat until the mixture is smooth. Divide the mixture between 2 *greased* 18cm sandwich tins and bake for 35 minutes.

When the cake has cooled, make the frosting. Put all the ingredients into a bowl and beat until frothy. Place the bowl over a pan of simmering water and whisk until mixture forms soft peaks. (Ensure you have adult assistance with this.)

Cover the whole cake with the white frosting, making swirly patterns and peaks. Decorate the sides with stars and crescent moons made from marzipan. Place small Lego astronauts on top of cake and a small flag to mark the First Footstep.

And to refresh your guests, some delicious **Moonshine**!

Ingredients

1 litre apple juice
600ml ginger ale
slices of apple and oranges

Simply mix the drinks together in a large jug and float the fruit slices on the top.

Somnium (the dream)

by Johannes Kepler, Late Imperial Mathematician
(written in 1609, published in 1634)

The whole of Levania [the Moon] does not exceed fourteen hundred German miles in circumference, that is, only a quarter of our Earth. Nevertheless, it has very high mountains as well as very deep and wide valleys; to this extent, it is much less of a perfect sphere than our Earth is. Yet it is all porous and, so to say, perforated with caves and grottoes everywhere, especially in the Provolvan region [the dark side of the Moon]; these recesses are the inhabitants' principle protection from heat and cold.

Whatever is born on the land or moves about on the land attains a monstrous size. Growth is very rapid. Everything has a short life, since it develops such an immensely massive body. The Provolvans have no fixed abode, no established home. In the course of one of their days they roam in crowds over their whole sphere, each according to his own nature: some use their hind legs, which far surpass those of our camels; some resort to wings; and some follow the receding water in boats; or, if a delay of several more days is necessary, then they crawl into caves. Most of them are divers; all of them, since they live naturally, draw their breath very slowly: hence under water they stay down at the bottom, helping nature with art. For in those very deep layers of the water, they say, the cold persists while the waves on top are heated up by the Sun; whatever clings to the surface is boiled out by the Sun at noon, and becomes food for the advancing hordes of wandering inhabitants.

> One of the first people to look at the Moon through a telescope at the beginning of the 17th Century was Sir William Lower. He said, "In full she appears like a tarte that my Cooke made me last Weeke, here a vaine of bright stuff, and there of dark, and so confused lie all over."

Those for whom breathing is more essential introduce the hot water into the caves through a narrow channel in order that it may flow a long time to reach the interior and cool off. There they shut themselves up for the greater part of the day, using the water for drink. When evening comes they go out, looking for food. In plants, the rind, in animals, the skin, or whatever replaces it, takes up the major portion of the bodily mass. It is spongy and porous. If anything is exposed during the day, it becomes hard and scorched; when evening comes, its husk drops off. Things born in the ground generally begin and end their lives on the same day, with new generations springing up daily.

Seleography is the branch of Astronomy which studies the Moon's surface.

The Headlines, July 1969

Colour of Moon in dispute

The Moon belongs to everyone

Just what is the Moon, anyway?

Old Moon theory on the rocks

Sacrilege, says Moon worshipper

Scientists split over Moonquake

Apollo Moon box opened

Pearl-like stone from Moon examined

Moon rock has glass bubbles

Moon has glassy skin and hot centre

Moondust reveals Sun's compositiion

Moon has hard layer over mush

Laserbeam from California bounces off mirror on Moon

British scientist gets Moon rock

Moon age surprises scientists

Moon may be all in pieces

Plants grow greener with lunar dust

Moon found to be as old as solar system

The Moon is older than itself

Quiz

1   What is *Gibbous*?
    ☐ a monkey
    ☐ the Moon between half and full
    ☐ talkative

2   What is *hell*?
    ☐ hot
    ☐ highlands extravehicular lunar landing
    ☐ a crater on the Moon

3   What is a *sinuous rille*?
    ☐ a frilly spacesuit
    ☐ a collapsed lava tube
    ☐ a flexible Moon drill

4 How long is a *lunar day*?
   □ 14 days
   □ 24 days
   □ 27 days 7 hours 43 minutes

5 When was the *countdown* first used?
   □ Apollo 1
   □ Luna 1
   □ a film called *The Woman in the Moon*

6 What is *albedo*?
   □ a crater on the Moon
   □ the Moon's power of reflection
   □ a white rabbit with a cold

7 What is *beer*?
   □ a crater on the Moon
   □ a drink
   □ backwards emergency exit rocket

8 What is (or are) *breccia*?
   □ freeze-dried rehydrateable breakfast
   □ space junk
   □ Moon rocks

9 What was the *'Eagle'*?
   □ Apollo 11's Lunar Module
   □ Apollo 11's Command Module
   □ a comic

10 What is *palus putredinis*?
   □ the Marsh of Decay
   □ the highest mountain on the Moon
   □ the White Rock

Answers:

1b; 2c; 3b; 4a; 5c; 6b; 7a; 8c; 9a; 10a

Reference books

The Moon our sister planet by Peter Cadogan (Cambridge University Press)
Man on the Moon by John Masefield (Constable)
Moon, Mars and meteorites by Peter Adams (HMSO for the British Geological Survey)
Spaceflight Magazine (British Inter-Planetary Society)
Nightwatch by Jane Burton and Kim Taylor (Michael Joseph)

On March 16, 1926 Robert Hutching Goddard launched the world's first liquid fuel rocket from a cabbage patch in Auburn, Massachusetts.

Some other Knight titles you may enjoy:

THE ENCYCLOPEDIA OF THE WORLDS OF DOCTOR WHO: A–D

DAVID SAUNDERS

How can 450,000 daffodils be connected with Doctor Who?
Where do the Cybermen come from?
Did Doctor Who travel in The Ark?

All the answers to your Doctor Who questions can be found in the first exciting volume of THE ENCYCLOPEDIA OF THE WORLDS OF DOCTOR WHO.

KNIGHT BOOKS

THE GHOST MESSENGERS

ROBERT SWINDELLS

Haunted by the ghosts of her grandfather and his war-time bomber crew, Meg tries to make sense of the warnings they give.

The development of a neglected piece of land into a conservation area adds to her super-natural experiences, which disturb her sleep and her school work.

What is the message – and will Meg be able to convince those around her of its importance?

"This well-plotted book . . . proceeds to a genuinely exciting climax."

Junior Bookshelf

KNIGHT BOOKS

SURVIVAL! A SCHOOL KID'S GUIDE

GLADYS OVER

DANGER SIGNS!
Do you feel unwell most Monday mornings, but
on top of the world on Friday afternoons?

Do your eyes water when it's liver and bacon for
lunch but light up when it's sausage and beans?

Are you revolted when your teacher asks you the
difference between a toad and an earthworm, but
revived when they suggest you might do a nature
study in the park for a change?

Then look out! These are the symptoms of a
severely distressed pupil. If you are to survive
school, you must take action right now.

APPROVED CURE:
Read this in-depth guide on how to last out until
the bell rings. Whether you suffer from
brainboxes, cheating, dinner ladies, ink pellets,
jelly or yawning, you need worry no longer. Here
is your essential SURVIVAL GUIDE.

KNIGHT BOOKS

FINGERS CROSSED

CHRIS POWLING

Is thirteen your lucky number?
If not, this book could change your mind!
Thirteen stories and thirteen poems specially
chosen by Chris Powling for this anthology will
delight you whether you go for something scary,
exciting, funny or sad.

KNIGHT BOOKS